THE 1

FOREPLAY

Thorsons
An imprint of HarperCollins Publishers
77–85 Fulham Palace Road
Hammersmith, London W6 8JB

Published in the UK by Thorsons 1999
1 3 5 7 9 10 8 6 4 2

Copyright © 1999 Godsfield Press
Text Copyright © 1999 Richard Craze

Produced for Thorsons by
Godsfield Press

Designed for Godsfield Press by
The Bridgewater Book Company

Photographs by Peter Pugh-Cook

Richard Craze asserts the moral right to be identified
as the author of this work.

A catalog record for this book is available from the British Library.
ISBN 0 7225 3832 4

Printed in Hong Kong

THE POCKET BOOK OF

FOREPLAY

Richard Craze

Thorsons
An Imprint of HarperCollins*Publishers*

CONTENTS

Introduction

So what is foreplay, and is it different from real sex? And what could we possibly teach you in a book about foreplay? Well, foreplay is everything you do with each other that isn't actual lovemaking – holding hands is foreplay (if done properly) and so is oral sex and masturbation (both singly and mutually). Foreplay carries on during lovemaking – and ideally afterward as well (then it becomes afterplay; see page 94). Foreplay can have orgasms in it or not – it depends on your own personal definition of what foreplay is.

new ideas

We all engage in foreplay in some form or another – it might just be kissing or several hours of intense and passionate foreplay of the sort you will find in this book – and we wouldn't dream of telling anyone what or how their foreplay should be.

However, good foreplay is constantly new, constantly stimulating and exciting. And that means new ideas, new experiences, and new challenges. Any relationship will grow stale over time if we don't work at it and make an effort to keep it vital and alive. Experiment, take a few chances. Explore all your senses – hearing, sight, taste, smell, and touch – as you get to know every corner of your partner's body. In *The Pocket Book of Foreplay* we offer suggestions and ideas for new things for you and your partner to try.

enjoying foreplay

Foreplay is an experience to be enjoyed – it isn't a race or a destination. You don't have to do it for any particular length of time or manage to try a specific number of new things. It is a pleasurable pastime that can lead to more enjoyable sexual relations – or simply be enjoyed for its own sake.

1

SETTING THE SCENE

Setting the scene

If you don't put in a little work beforehand, the experience of foreplay can feel somehow lacking or unsatisfactory. Over the next few pages we offer suggestions for how you can set the scene. This isn't about getting anyone to do anything they don't want to. This is about a loving couple making an effort to create the right atmosphere for foreplay – an atmosphere in which you will both feel relaxed, comfortable, loved, safe, and sexy.

foreplay as intimacy

Except for making love, foreplay is the most intimate contact we will have with another person – and it therefore makes sense to make sure that it is special. We need to take time and trouble over and with our partner if we want them to feel that they can trust us sexually and emotionally and be relaxed enough to really indulge all their passions. If they need to rest first after a long day, let them. If we rush them, pressure them, or give them insufficient time and care, they won't feel as good about foreplay as they might. Setting the scene and creating the right atmosphere is taking that time and care.

Bathing

If your lover feels hot, tired, irritable, and unclean, they simply won't want to make love. If they are hot and in need of a bath, run it for them and pamper them beyond their wildest dreams. Simply putting the plug in and filling the bathtub with hot water isn't bathing – nor is it pampering your lover. You have to create an entire stage setting, beginning with the lighting.

Electric lights are seldom sexy, erotic, or discreet – merely harsh. Candlelight, on the other hand, is sexy and makes us look a lot better. Fill the bathroom with candles and turn off all the other lights.

essential oils

Hot water on its own isn't particularly sexy – just wet. Try adding some essential aromatherapy oils (ylang-ylang for lust, rose for love, and pennyroyal for stamina) to create the right smells, to provide an erotic oily texture to the water, and to give it a little discreet coloring.

Provide warm towels, and lots of them. Make sure the room is warm enough – and prepared enough. Put away children's toys – this is a room being made ready for sexy grownups to do sexy things. Burn a little incense in the room for a smoky, erotic atmosphere – and then call your lover. Let them soak. Let them read. Let them do whatever they like to do in a bath. Wash their hair for them. Scrub their back. Scrub any area they want washed more than others. Bring them wine and grapes.

drying them off

Help them get out when they have relaxed enough. Wrap them in luxurious warm towels and dry them off – paying special attention to certain parts.

• Having a warm, leisurely bath washes away inhibitions.

Grooming

When your lover is all clean from their glorious bath, it's time to start grooming them. Dry their hair for them. Brush it and make it gleam and shine. After a hot bath they may need to be oiled all over. Use a few drops of essential oil in a neutral base such as grapeseed oil and then slowly, lingeringly, rub it into every inch of their skin.

Take your time and don't touch any erotic areas – not yet, anyway. The whole experience of being oiled is so sexy that it will make your lover want to go further – and nothing is so exquisitely teasing as moving your fingers toward their sexy parts and then not touching them. They will squirm and possibly even beg – but don't give in to their desire – not yet. Foreplay is all about teasing and bringing desire up to its

maximum. Timing is important, and so is tantalizing your partner. If they don't want to be oiled they may prefer talcum powder. You can powder them all over and enjoy slowly smoothing their skin with it. The same rules apply – don't touch any sexy parts at this stage.

getting dressed

After drying and oiling them (or powdering them) you can help them get dressed. If you are going out they may like to wear their best clothes – but if you are staying in for a night of passion, you can help them get dressed up in their sexiest outfit – whatever it is they wear to turn you on. Getting dressed is all part of foreplay.

• Prepare for a night of passionate lovemaking by pampering your lover with a slow, sensuous shave.

Sit your lover in front of a mirror while you slowly draw sensuous clothes up over their skin. Let your fingers lovingly and lingeringly caress each and every bit of their body as fabrics are rubbed across nipples and buttocks.

• Brushing or combing hair in long, leisurely strokes is a gentle and intimate initiation to foreplay.

Creating the mood

No one responds well to quick and hurried sex – and no one responds well to sex that isn't intimate, loving, and caring. If you want your partner to feel responsive, you need to sow the seeds of their desire a long time in advance. To be a great lover it is necessary to be kind, compassionate, gentle, caring, and genuinely interested in your sexual partner as both a friend and an equal. To create the right mood for foreplay or sex you have to be aware of their mood. To be aware of their mood you have to share in it, be part of it, and help to change it if it is unhappy or negative.

turn down the lights

Many couples think that sex begins with a simple turning down of the lights – as if this is a code lovers use to signify the beginning of passion. It's not enough.

Good sex begins with concern for your partner. Creating the mood is knowing what turns them on – it might be turning down the lights, but it's probably a lot more complex than that.

simply touching

If you haven't touched your partner in a nonsexual way all day, then don't expect them to respond well if you suddenly touch them in a sexual way. Sexual touching should grow out of holding hands, hugging, kissing, and generally being close and intimate in a warm and loving way. If you are permanently creating the mood by being close, you won't have to create the mood now – it will already be part of the scene.

• Skin-to-skin contact helps to build a relaxed, intimate mood with an erotic edge.

Atmosphere

If you and your lover have been tender and lovingly close all day, you will be prepared for sex and foreplay whenever the mood takes you. But is the atmosphere right? Harsh electric lights, an unmade bed, clothes strewn all over the floor, a pile of dirty cups by the bedside, and you unwashed, unprepared unperfumed, and unready – these are not going to turn anybody on.

turning the bedroom into the boudoir

Good foreplay takes place not in a bedroom but in a boudoir. Same room, same place, completely different feeling. Light it with candles. Make the bed with clean, fresh, crisp sheets. Put away all the clothes. Tidy up. Light some incense. Wash, bathe, and groom yourself (or do it with your lover). Dress provocatively and smell as clean and fresh as possible. Pay particular attention to oral hygiene – no one likes to be kissed by someone with bad breath.

music and food

Good foreplay shouldn't be rushed or hurried. Choose some light refreshments – you're going to be here for some time – good wine and some nibbles (other than your lover, that is). Have some gentle and

sexy music playing in the background.
You probably know which particular style
of music or which artist turns your partner
on. If you don't, find out. If possible,
make sure that the music plays continu-
ally; there is nothing worse than having
to get up to change a CD or tape at
a crucial moment.

You can create your boudoir
anywhere – it doesn't have to be
the bedroom. But it does have to be
prepared and have the right atmosphere.
The key word here is *subtlety* – make the
lighting, music, and furnishings discreet
and refined, sexy but elegant.

• Create the right atmosphere for lovemaking with
fresh, clean sheets, sexy music playing in the
background, and subtle lighting.

Sexy gifts

Giving a token of love to your lover is part of a very old tradition – and one that shouldn't be allowed to fall into disuse. Giving a sexy gift isn't the same as giving a birthday present or a surprise present at some other time – this is about foreplay and giving a surprise specifically for sexiness. You don't have to be extravagant or lavish – just thoughtful and enterprising.

thinking of you

Knowing someone has been thinking about you enough, in a sexy way, to go out and buy something erotic for your pleasure can be a real turn-on, since it shows they care about more than just gratifying their immediate desires. And you can show you also care by choosing a special sexy gift for your lover. You could buy underwear for each other, but most women say that most men usually get it wrong. So you might want to save that for another time; unless of course you both go out shopping together – and then that's further opportunity for foreplay (see page 72).

naughty and shocking

But what about a set of handcuffs?
Naughty and shocking perhaps, but
also deliciously
sexy, even if you
never actually
get around to
using them. Or
you could sur-
prise each other
with sexy food, such
as a chocolate penis, fresh figs, or bananas
covered with cream. Or how about a set of
flavored condoms? Or even ribbed or
shaped ones? Vibrators can make good
sexy gifts, and you can have all the fun of
choosing them together. Or try
going for a single red rose for a real
classy effect.

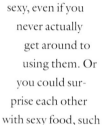

• The delicious texture of luxurious silk and satin is irresistible.

Taking time

Foreplay shouldn't be rushed – ever. It is a time of pleasure, of enjoyment. If you're not enjoying yourself you shouldn't be doing it – and if you are enjoying yourself, why stop?

cooking a special meal

Taking time means preparation and effort. Cook a special meal for your lover, dress appropriately, light the table with candles, open the finest wine you can afford, set out your best tableware, put out fresh clean napkins – then flirt outrageously during the meal. Couples who have good foreplay and lovemaking flirt with each other a lot. Most of us flirt when we first meet, but it often goes by the wayside once the relationship gets going. It shouldn't.

emotional stroking

Rushed foreplay will leave your lover feeling unsatisfied. If we rush, we aren't providing the emotional caressing they need. Make sure that when you are going to make love, fool around, or just kiss and cuddle, there are no interruptions – your lover is special and shouldn't just be fitted in. Take time and take effort and care and you will be rewarded by an increase in not only the quantity of foreplay but, more important, the quality.

• Dining by candlelight may be traditional, but it's a failsafe way to set the scene.

2

Spontaneous foreplay

Once we get into a relationship, it is easy to get into a routine of foreplay that quickly becomes boring – and that means unsatisfactory. The answer is not another lover who will spice up our sex life – we already have one. What we need to do is expand and experiment with our foreplay to put the sparkle and excitement back into our love life.

acting out fantasies

Foreplay, like most sex, goes on primarily in the mind. It is about acting out fantasies, being teased and turned on, being excited, looking forward to, anticipating, and wanting to explore more. The actual physical side of foreplay is easy – we all know which parts go where. But for adventurous foreplay we need to start being a bit more daring, a bit more spontaneous.

going further

We all have certain places we'd like to make love, either because we have never tried it there or because we have, loved it, and want to do it again. In the next few pages we will look at some of these places and offer some suggestions as to how you can go about it successfully, safely, and satisfactorily – you don't have to limit yourself to the bedroom.

In the office

There is something so sexy about making love on an office desk that it figures in most people's fantasies at some time or another. The thought of being seduced by your boss or vice versa can be very erotic. Just imagine being called in to take a letter or file something and finding yourself laid out, exposed, and wanton on the polished smoothness of an old oak desk.

making it work

If you and your partner work together you will have considerably more opportunity to play out this fantasy than if you don't. But even if you don't, you can still have fun with the office fantasy. You can set up a desk at home. One of you can be

• Intimacy in the formal surroundings of an office is always tantalizing.

the boss and the other the employee. Take turns giving the orders. You will both need to dress up for this – business suits and no underwear. Call in your secretary. Tell them you want something taken down – and then take it down. Or be the secretary and pop into the

boss's office to borrow a file; then drop it into their lap and insist on retrieving it – with your teeth.

not just the desk

You don't have to have sex on a desk or on the executive-class carpet to act out an office foreplay fantasy – what about in the elevator? Or behind the filing cabinets? In the computer room? And you don't have to be boss and worker – try out other roles, such as bike courier and receptionist. Or how about being the cleaners and polishing everything in a new and novel way?

• For an authentic office fantasy, call each other by formal names (Ms. Brown, Mr. Smith).

In the bedroom

Bedrooms have beds for making love and sleeping in. They should be friendly places where you'd like to spend time with your lover, reading, fooling around, relaxing, and eating. They should be private, sensual, and very sexy. Bedrooms also have lots of props you can make good use of for foreplay. Pillows, for instance – you can have nude pillow fights, and think of how many lovemaking positions require a pillow.

in the closet

Most bedrooms have closets. Ever tried foreplay in the darkness of a closet? No? Then do so and see how far you can go. What about making love *under* the bed for a change? Or, if there isn't room, next to the bed? Or in the doorway to the bedroom? Or how about in front of the bedroom mirror? Or in the bedroom chair? On a heap of pillows?

the sultan's palace

Don't be confined by your bedroom's physical dimensions. Use your imagination. You could challenge your partner to turn the bedroom into your favorite fantasy – the bed could become a schooner in full sail for that pirate fantasy; a sultan's harem; a dungeon of exquisite torture; the lifeboat of a sinking ship – or even the island you get marooned on.

• Pillows are great bedroom props; nude pillow fights are an exhilarating way to start a night of vigorous lovemaking.

In the kitchen

Kitchens are not only useful for cooking and eating – they also provide lots of opportunities for erotic and sexy games. Many men have fantasies of making love to their partners while they are bent over the sink – why not indulge them, and then change places.

dish of the day

You can use the kitchen table – just make sure it is strong enough and clear away the clutter first. You can cook for each other, in the nude of course. Or how about serving yourself up as the main dish? You could lie on the table and decorate all your erogenous zones with

suitable food – how about lots of cream and strawberries? Or you could get your lover to lie on the table and then decorate them – and then eat all the food off them. Choose food that has a texture, shape, or taste that turns you on.

• The kitchen can be the scene of a variety of exciting encounters.

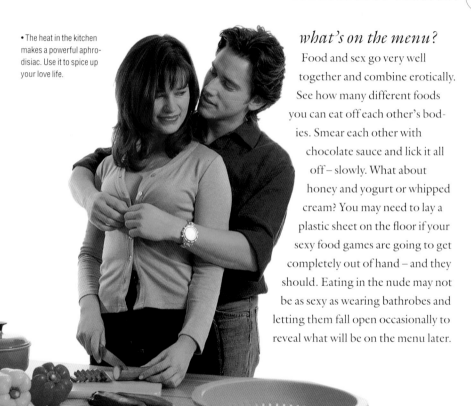

• The heat in the kitchen makes a powerful aphrodisiac. Use it to spice up your love life.

what's on the menu?

Food and sex go very well together and combine erotically. See how many different foods you can eat off each other's bodies. Smear each other with chocolate sauce and lick it all off – slowly. What about honey and yogurt or whipped cream? You may need to lay a plastic sheet on the floor if your sexy food games are going to get completely out of hand – and they should. Eating in the nude may not be as sexy as wearing bathrobes and letting them fall open occasionally to reveal what will be on the menu later.

Backseat of the car

Unless you have a stretch limousine or spacious station wagon, trying to make love on the backseat of a car will always be difficult, if not impossible. But there is a lot you can do without having to go the whole way. First, though, you have to find somewhere to park the car.

getting caught

The thrill of being seen or getting caught may be part of your fantasy and add to your enjoyment of foreplay – but you also have to be aware of any legal restraints about having sex in public wherever you live. If you have any doubts, you can always park in your own driveway and go for it. Watch out for nosy neighbors. Tune you car radio to a suitable station or make your own tape to suit the mood.

being realistic

We've all seen movies in which a couple has wild and abandoned sex on the backseat of a car – and then when we try it, it doesn't seem to work quite so well. It's uncomfortable, there's no room, it's cold, the gear shift stabs us in the back of the leg, the window handle jams in our ear. We need to be realistic. Hollywood makes things happen that simply aren't real. Don't expect to have the same sex as in

• Steamy windows may remind you of your high school or college days.

the movies – but you can have some great foreplay. Bringing each other to orgasm by using fingers, lips, and tongues is so much more fun – and achievable. Take turns to lie back and be caressed, sucked, licked, massaged, and stroked – and you can keep an eye out for those nosy neighbors at the same time!

Talking dirty

We all need to be told we are loved – but we also need to hear that we are sexy, desirable, and stimulating. We need to be reassured that the old magic still works. And if *we* need to be reassured, then chances are our partner needs it as well. So do it.

which parts?

There is something very erotic about someone whispering naughty things in your ear, telling you all the things they would like to do to you – and with you – later on. At the restaurant having a business meal with your partner and lots of colleagues, lean over and say exactly which parts you'd like to lick later on – and which ones you are going to suck and kiss. They'll probably be unable to eat a single thing.

keep it up

Don't go all silent during foreplay and lovemaking. If you talk to your partner normally during the day, why not talk to them during sex as well? Tell them what you are doing as you do it. Most people get turned on by their lover talking dirty to them while they are making love. You don't have to be crude or explicit. Just use your voice in the same way as you would use your fingers, lips, and tongue.

• Talk dirty to me or talk nice – either way can be a turn-on.

Role play

Increasingly in modern sexuality the boundaries between the sexes are getting blurred. No longer is the man the dominant partner and controlling the sexual agenda. Women's sexuality is as strong and as complex as men's. If you get stuck in traditional sexual roles, you miss valuable and exciting opportunities to explore foreplay as an adventure. By swapping roles, you get to experience your partner's side of things as well as opening up your own sexuality.

swapping clothes, swapping roles

Clothing and makeup go a long way toward defining our gender and sexuality. So simply try swapping. There is nothing to be lost except your own preconceived notions of what is right or wrong, what is correct or "normal." Once you begin breaking taboos about gender and roles,

• Strict Teacher and Naughty Boy are popular roles.

you can unlock many delightful aspects of foreplay. Dress up in each other's clothes for sex and see how it affects you. Do you become more dominant in his suit? Do you feel more feminine in her sexy lingerie? How does it affect your partner? You may find it a turn-off, in which case you don't need to do it again – or conversely, you may find it very sexy. You won't know unless you try.

swapping character

Swapping roles may change your perception of who dominates the partnership, and free you up to explore different ways to interact. If one of you always initiates sex play, try letting the other partner do it for a change – or if one of you always chooses the location, let the other choose.

• Whatever role you play, both of you should agree on limits beforehand.

3

THE LOVING TOUCH

The loving touch

If we're going to share good foreplay and really go with our lover to new and exciting heights of passion, we have to practice – and what better practice could we have than with our lover? We need to know their body and their responses pretty intimately if we are going to give them maximum pleasure. And by touching them – a lot – we will learn fast and become more adept at foreplay.

touching

Over the next few pages we will look at some ways of getting in touch and staying in touch with our lover. Through touch we communicate a lot without consciously realizing it. If our touch is hesitant or restrained, our lover will know there is something not quite right. If our touch is bold and warm, they will feel loved and reassured.

caressing, embracing, and kissing

Good foreplay is not about being able to excite your partner by knowing how to stimulate their genitalia. Really good foreplay is just as much about emotional stroking as physical stroking. It involves as much emotional touching as hands-on touching. You're more likely to have great sex if you're having great love as well.

Kissing

Our lips are incredibly sensitive. It's something to do with the wetness – and lots of nerve endings, of course. And there are two sorts of kisses – kisses of love, and kisses of lust. They overlap at times. The ones we are interested in here are the kisses of love – you'll have to wait until the following pages for the kisses of lust.

kisses of love

The kisses you'd give a small child are the kisses of love – gentle, affectionate, and caring. And these kisses are also the kisses you should be giving your lover. This doesn't mean you should treat them as a child – but your kisses should convey all the love you feel in that one small, moist expression of care. Kiss them gently on the back of the neck when they aren't expecting it. Kiss their hands and fingers. Kiss the

• Kissing any part of the face is always an intimate experience.

• Explore each other's lips; the corners of the mouth are especially sensitive.

backs of their knees and the soles of their feet. The poet Elizabeth Barrett Browning knew what she was talking about when she wrote the following lines about her husband Robert:

> *First time he kissed me, he but only*
> *kissed the fingers of this hand wherewith*
> *I write; And, ever since, it grew more*
> *clean and white.*

butterfly kisses

Kiss every inch of your lover's face with tiny, delicate butterfly kisses – kisses so light and gentle they can barely, scarcely be felt. Watch your lover go wild with love. Use your fluttering eyelids for more butterfly kisses. Kiss your lover behind the ears and on their eyelids. Kiss them moistly, wetly – and often.

• Gently rubbing faces can be very arousing.

Deep kissing

The Chinese won't kiss in public because they think that kissing is too erotic, too sexy for public display. They could be right, if your kisses are erotic enough. We all know how to kiss, but do we do it long enough? Deep enough? Often enough?

lusty kisses

For kisses to be truly lusty and to really turn our partner on, they need to be very passionate. They should be done not only with your lips but also with your tongue, your teeth, your heart, and your soul. If you practice kissing well enough it might just be possible to make your lover reach orgasm by kissing alone – now there's an option worth trying. Kissing with tongues used to be called French kissing, but surely it is now universal? Tongues can be sucked gently or ferociously. Get you lover to stick their tongue out while you suck on it. Kiss, and keep kissing, as they reach orgasm, and see how sucking on their tongue heightens the experience. Get them to do the same to you. Kiss for a long time, explore every part of your partner's mouth – under the top lip, the root of the tongue. Kiss with your mouths wide open, and enjoy the wetness that you generate.

kissing the erotic areas

We will look at oral sex a bit later on (see pages 84–87), but it's worth practicing kissing the erotic areas without it having to lead to full-on sex. A man kissing a woman's breasts can be sexy fore-play, an act of love or an act of worship and devotion. Similarly, a woman kissing a man's penis has all sorts of pos-sibilities.

• Spend a long time kissing; it makes orgasm much more enjoyable.

Licking and sucking

These two go hand in hand. You can have licking without sucking – but why?
We all like to be licked and we all like to be sucked. Our skin responds well
to moist caresses from our partner's tongue and lips, and good foreplay is all
about getting the best responses.

how well do you know them?

So, just how well do you know your lover's
body? Pretty well, you probably think. It
might be fun to test your knowledge.
Which parts do they like having licked?
And which parts do they like having
sucked? Don't ask them – try them out.
Lick and suck every inch of their body to
see their response. Tell them it's a clinical
experiment. Play doctor and patient while
you are at it. And vary the pressure you

use, the amount of wetness, the time spent
on each part. Find out which nipple is more

• Don't neglect any area of your partner's body.

• Behind the ears is an erotic zone for many.

how much licking can they stand?

Can your lover come just by your licking their nipples? Try it, and keep at it until they do – or ask you to move on to another part. Have you found any areas that they positively hate having licked or sucked? Probably not, but you will find out which ones they prefer.

• The throat is especially sensitive, particularly at the base.

sensitive. Find out which toe enjoys being sucked the most. Explore those forgotten nooks and crannies with your tongue until your partner begs you to stop – or go on.

Intimacy

Intimacy and closeness are very similar, but closeness is about being caring and intimacy is about being at ease with your lover. Closeness is talking after making love; intimacy is what you talk about.

an intimate bonus

Being intimate with another person, being that free, is a difficult thing to do with a stranger. You have to know someone pretty well to relax completely with them. Being intimate is one of the many bonuses of having a stable, long-term relationship with one person. You can tell them anything and they won't take it the wrong way, be offended, be shocked or feel confronted, or be judgmental. You can share your fantasies – and theirs. You can tell

them all the things you've longed to do but never had the courage, equipment, inclination, or stamina – and they won't laugh or think you are mad or dangerous.

being friends

Intimacy is the same as friendship in many ways. The more we are friends with our lover, the more we can open up sexually with them. If we are reserved with strangers and open with friends, it makes sense to be friends with our lover.

Being intimate is being comfortable around each other, which means being able to walk around in the nude and not feel embarrassed. Once we are intimate and comfortable, it is easier to be intimate and sexual. Most people are wary of baring their soul, even to an established partner. Take time to build an intimate relationship.

• Use intimate moments to tell each other what you like and what you want from each other.

Caressing

In its most basic form caressing is moving your hands over your lover's body – that's it. But without passion, arousal, and lust, it ain't foreplay. Spend time exploring the thrill of different touches, different ways of stroking and exploring.

wanting to, and enjoying

There has to be desire and affection in your caressing or your partner will be able to detect the absence. You have to genuinely enjoy caressing, and want to caress, your lover. If you're just going through the motions so that they will be aroused and then you can have sex with them, it will fail. Caressing isn't just stroking this part or nibbling that one to a set pattern or routine in order to get your partner in the mood. Caressing is an art form in itself – everything from fondling to stroking, tickling to cuddling – it's all caressing and it all takes time and should be given your full attention.

two-way thing

Your fingers are very sensitive. Except for your lips, they are probably the most sensitive parts of your body, and while you are giving caresses you are receiving information subconsciously. If you aren't caressing your lover's body in its entirety you will miss some of the delicious clues and signs that they are transmitting about how aroused they are, how close to coming, how much they want to be kissed or caressed in a particular place. Caressing is a two-way thing, a channel for sensual communication. If you don't do it, you miss out just as much as your lover.

• Let your fingers pick up the messages from your partner's body.

Massage to relax

We're not talking acupressure here – nor are we in the business of therapeutic massage to ease aches and sprains, although that may well be a side effect and bonus. What we are interested in is massage as a form of relaxation prior to foreplay.

getting well oiled

There's nothing more relaxing than having your lover's hands rubbing sensuously along your skin, stroking and caressing. So don't think about giving a massage to remedy a sports injury or correct a back problem, and really let yourself go. You will need a naked lover, some baby oil or something like it (a neutral nonallergenic oil is best, but add a few drops of sensuous essential oil if you like – rose, ylang-ylang, neroli, vanilla), a cleanable surface to work on (plastic sheeting is sexy – so is plastic wrap, but you can't get it big enough), and lots of tissues or big warm towels to clean each other with afterward.

massage techniques

What you need is enthusiasm, confidence, and a sense of fun. Get your lover to begin by lying face down. Spread oil on their back and rub it all in. It isn't a good idea to pour cold oil on them, so warm it up first in your hands. Use your hands to rub gently.

Spread the oil around so you see it soaking in – then you can see any bits you've missed. Get your lover to turn over, and then you can begin with their legs and work upward. Leave out the genitals and do their stomach and chest or breasts. When they are ready you can go back and massage those areas they really want you to. Take your time and don't rub oil in anywhere it might be harmful.

• Take turns indulging each other in a sensual all-over body massage.

Massage to arouse

Once your lover is well oiled, relaxed, and ready, it might be time to massage all those parts you skipped when you were massaging to relax your lover. Now it's time to go back and massage the erotic areas.

for men

Your partner's breasts and vulva are the obviously erotic places to massage, but don't forget that she will also feel aroused if you massage the backs of her thighs, her buttocks, and her feet. She may also have her own preferences, and you will need to experiment – a lot – to find out where all her sensuous zones are. If you scent your massage oil with essential oils, be very careful of sensitive areas and stop immediately if your partner reports discomfort.

• Don't rub too hard; the idea is to arouse, not overstimulate.

for women

Obviously, your partner's penis is what needs massaging most when you are massaging to arouse – but don't go too far or he'll come and then want to fall asleep. The art of giving an arousing massage is to arouse – and hold the arousal. Once you start massaging his penis he might not want you to stop. Best to concentrate – initially – on other areas: the underside of his scrotum, his perineum, his pubic region. You can tug lightly at his pubic hair, his nipples, and any other areas he may especially favor.

for both of you

An arousing massage should be slow, gentle, and very teasing. Use lots of oil and stroke sensuously and erotically. Don't rub

• Gentle pressure on the nape of the neck is guaranteed to arouse.

too hard or use movements that are too soft or light. Most men like to be handled firmly, while most women like a more gentle approach. Whether you include orgasm in your sexy massage is entirely up to you, but an arousing massage, as foreplay, is certainly a good way to get ready for sex.

Listening and loving

Sometimes a close, intimate look may be all you need to get your lover's pulse racing; sometimes just the merest touch can have the same effect. But you won't get arousal or excitement if you don't know and understand your lover.

listening

Being good at foreplay – and at making love – means having an almost instinctive knowledge of your lover. If you listen to the tiny signals being given off, then you will be able to gauge their mood effectively. It's no good going for it if they are tired, depressed, hungry, or preoccupied. Listen to them. If they are animated about their day at work, then pay attention and hear what they are saying.

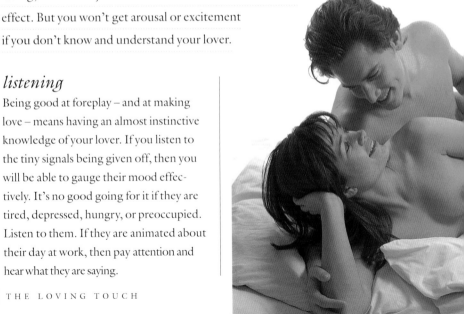

loving

Loving means caring, nurturing, and being free with your lover. Try to read their mood. Share interests with them. Share secrets with them. Share their hopes and dreams, goals and aspirations. If you only touch them in a sexual way, they will feel uneasy, valued only as sex objects, two-dimensional characters. If you touch them in a reassuringly loving way, they will feel safe and relaxed with you. Foreplay doesn't begin when you get your clothes off and into bed – it begins when you smile at each other, hold hands, feel good around each other, and take care of each other. The world's best lovers have always been great confidants and conversationalists, genuinely interested in each other as people, as much as in making love to them.

and afterward?

Keep listening; keep loving. Hold them, reassure them, be with them, be present. Don't ever turn away.

• Listen to your partner and find out their needs and desires – sharing and caring makes for better lovemaking.

4

EROTIC FOREPLAY

Erotic foreplay

Once we get beyond the basics of foreplay, we want to know what to do to spice it up a bit. In the previous sections we have looked at ways of getting foreplay to work on an emotional and deep level; in the next sections we will look at ways of getting it to work on physical and sensual levels – what you can do and how you can do it.

which parts go where

Good erotic foreplay isn't just about trying to do as many sexy things as possible with your partner – foreplay is also about getting your lover and yourself to open up sexually. Making an effort to understand how and what turns your lover on is important, as much so as pushing back the boundaries, exploring all kinds of fantasies together, and keeping things fresh.

turning each other on

Good foreplay means putting in some effort – though it shouldn't feel like work but an extremely enjoyable task. Turning your lover on is a privilege and should be a delight. Don't be afraid to experiment and explore fantasies together. Arousing your lover in new and exciting ways can give you a wonderful sense of power – and keep you closer together as a couple.

Seduction

Seduction isn't getting someone to do something they don't want to – in fact, it's about showing respect. Showing them that you care sufficiently to take time and trouble to get them to take their clothes off and into bed with you. That you value them enough to want them to be with you sexually, and that you are prepared to think about them, flirt with them, encourage them, and nurture them sexually.

I want to be seduced by you

We all want to be seduced. No one responds well to a quick fondle and a demand for sex. We all like to be wooed and won. Seducing our partner isn't a chore or manipulation – it's a pleasure and a treat. When we undress a lover it should be done slowly and with great delicacy – it's no good just ripping off buttons and clothes and then launching into sex as quickly as possible. There may be a place for the sudden "take-me-quickly-right-here-and-now" approach – but not all the time. If you and your partner haven't seen each other for a long time, for instance, it can be overwhelming to feel the buttons fly off and the T-shirt rip as you come together.

getting it right

You have to provide the right ambience,
mood, warmth, safety, and a relaxing
and sensuously dreamy atmosphere for
seduction to work. You have to make
sure the candles are replaced, the
incense is lit, the bed (or wherever)
is clean and comfortable, the
clothes are sexy and elegant. No one
wants to be seduced when they're
not looking their best, so give your
lover time to prepare and get
themselves ready. And most of
all, give them lots of time – a
hurried seduction is worse
than no seduction at all.

• Taking off each other's
clothes, slowly, adds great
excitement to lovemaking.

Dressing up

What does your lover like you to wear when you make love or indulge in some serious fooling around? Sensuous and silky underwear? A fireman's helmet? A nurse's outfit? An elegant tailored suit? If you know, how often do you wear it? If you don't know, why not?

• The partially clothed body can be far more erotic than the nude.

you have to wear something

Dressing up for our lover isn't pandering to their sexual perversions. It's a caring and sensitive thing true lovers do. To allow them to enjoy your foreplay together in a nonjudgmental way is probably the first and best step you can take to giving them the trust and sexual respect they ought to have. If you reject your lover's choice of love-wear, then you also are rejecting them – albeit unconsciously. If you judge them in a negative way, it shows. After all, you have to wear something – unless you only ever make love or have foreplay in the nude.

wearing the monkey suit

If what they want you to wear is impractical – a full gorilla costume, for instance – couldn't you somehow compromise and wear it occasionally or just wear the head in bed? And what about you? What do you want them to wear? And do you feel rejected when they won't? Dressing up for your lover is fine. It's sexy and caring. Dressing up is also fun, and that is an important part of foreplay. If you don't enjoy it, you don't need to do it again, but you ought to try it before you decide.

• The combination of refined lace and bare flesh is powerfully arousing.

Fetishism

We're not talking real fetishism here – as when someone can't achieve orgasm unless they or their partner is always wearing a particular article of clothing or fabric. What we are doing is playing around with various toys and props to see the effect they have and to enhance foreplay in a fun way.

favorites

Most of us have some fabric we find especially sexy. It might be silk or satin, rubber, plastic, leather, feathers, or fur – and there is nothing wrong with incorporating that fabric into our foreplay. If you want your lover dressed from head to foot in plastic wrap or silk bandages, it doesn't do any harm to try this out from time to time (be careful to leave a breathing hole). The only real problem with serious fetishism is when one lover is incapable of being sexual without the help of that particular fetish – and their lover disapproves or won't cooperate for some

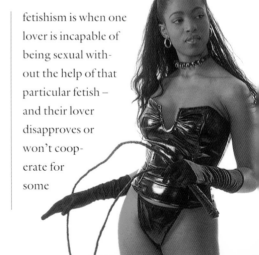

other reason. Indulging ourselves occasionally is not only a pleasurable experience but can also be beneficial, because it
acts as an outlet for deep sexual desires.
Enjoy your favorites.

going along with it

If your lover suggests a particular fetish
that they like – you wearing satin corsets
or riding boots or a loin cloth, for exam-
ple – don't reject it without first giving it a
try. Go along with it even if you think that
it's too silly for words, bizarre, or eccentric.
You never know – you might actually like
it, and besides, if it's what your partner
wants, then out of respect you should give
it a real try.

• Indulge each other's fetishes. If rubber corsets and thigh-length
boots have always been your partner's fantasy, then give it a try.

Etiquette

Foreplay etiquette is a code that allows you and your partner to feel safe and trusting with each other, knowing that neither of you is going to press for or demand anything that is too extreme or unhealthy or unhygienic. Etiquette is making sure your partner is completely happy to go along with your desire and fantasies.

ask first

You should always be able to voice what it is you want to do sexually. If you don't ask, you'll never know if it is acceptable. You may not like the answer, but at least you'll know. Perhaps one of your desires is to play out some mild bondage fantasy. You suggest it and your partner is horrified – they'd never thought of anything like that before. Foreplay etiquette means you don't put pressure on them, blackmail them, threaten them, or coerce them unduly. You suggest, they reject. Later they may come back to you and say that they've thought about it and wouldn't mind trying a moderated version because they know they are quite safe with you. If you want reassurance, figure out an agreed code word to be used if either of you wants to end the fantasy.

sharing ideas

It's okay to try out new things. It's okay to experiment. It's okay to suggest sexy games. What is not okay is to get your partner to do anything they really don't want to – nor is it okay to reject anything they want just because it doesn't really turn you on. You have a responsibility to them sexually to provide maximum pleasure – and whatever they want that contributes to that pleasure is fine. Don't be judgmental of another's fantasies – yours may seem just as strange to them.

• Share erotic literature and photography for mutual stimulation.

Public foreplay

There's no doubt about it – having full sex in public really is a no-no. It shocks people. It is illegal in most places. It is too much, too extreme, too confrontational. However, a little fooling around in public is sexy and arousing.

a quick flash

There is something deliciously naughty about flashing each other in public – it might only be a quick glimpse of underwear, a little piece of flesh that wouldn't normally be seen, a sudden exposing of a breast or nipple – but it works as foreplay. You could go out and forget the underwear and see who can show the other the most without getting caught or seen. You can wear outer clothes that completely hide what's underneath – but wear nothing underneath and make sure your partner sees that nothingness. Invent secret code words that only you and your partner will recognize, and bring your shared code words into conversations where others are present.

going further

How far you are prepared to go in public is entirely up to you and your lover. Some couples like a quick fondle, and that's fine for them. Others like to go a

whole lot further and see if they can bring each other to orgasm without being observed. You could go to the movies together and fool around like you did when you were both teenagers – and if you didn't, then try it for the first time – it's fun. Try fooling around in the car – but not while driving. Go to the park and fool around on a park bench – it's amazing how far you can go without anyone realizing. Take a train journey, a night bus trip, or a short flight and see what you can get up to. Use the time between stops, take a travel blanket to cover up, find hidden corners to play in.

• Foreplay in public carries its own naughty thrill for lovers. Just don't go all the way.

Visual foreplay

Visual stimulation may be more important for men than for women – at least that is what was always thought. Not true. Women need as much visual stimulation as men – it's just that they may like it to be a little more discreet, a little less obvious. Try a little finesse.

what to show

There's no doubt most men get turned on by the sight of their lover half undressed or dressed provocatively. Women seem to get more turned on by seeing their lover dressed elegantly or looking a little macho. You know your lover and will know what turns them on. Show them what they like to see. Taking your clothes off for them

• Learn to draw attention to erogenous zones without removing a stitch.

can be done languidly, sexily, slowly, eroti-cally, and arousingly. There's no harm in it. Some people seem to think that doing a "striptease" for their lover is somehow tacky or cheap. It isn't if it's done well. You don't have to rush out and buy lots of thongs or sequins. Just take your clothes off as you would do anyway – but do it for them, looking straight at them in a sexy way. If you are not sure how to do it, look at movies, or even go to a strip show. If you like dancing, incorporate your strip into a favorite routine – it's a lot easier to do it to music, even if the music is just in your head.

how far to go

You can tell your partner what it is you really like to see. It's a whole lot easier for them if you tell them – or they may never

get it right. Displaying your body to your lover should be easy, but we all suffer from a neg-ative view of what we look like – too fat, too old, too saggy, too many lines. Your lover, however, may not feel any of that about you – so show it and make them happy.

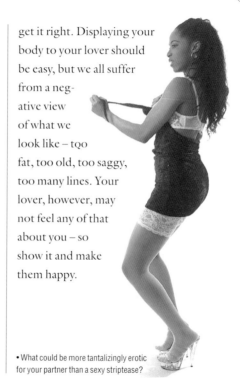

• What could be more tantalizingly erotic for your partner than a sexy striptease?

Teasing

Teasing during foreplay is getting your partner excited when there's nothing they can do about it. It's exquisite torture and very arousing. It gets the juices flowing for later and is an essential part of lovemaking.

physical flirting

Teasing can be physical flirting – the occasional touch in public, the fondling when no one's looking, the sexy phone call when they're in a meeting, the quick flash of sexy underwear just as they look back to wave goodbye. We usually flirt with our eyes and voice. Teasing is flirting with our touch and hands and body. Teasing is letting them see what's on offer later – but they can't have it now, or touch or anything. Teasing isn't cruel, it's fun. Teasing isn't holding out an option and then withdrawing it; quite the reverse. It's holding out an option that they know you are promising for later. Teasing is delayed sex, not withheld sex.

when to tease

Tease your lover when there is nothing they can do about it. That's what usually gets them going more quickly than anything. And you don't have to show them anything actually – just licking your lips may be enough. Wait until they're talking to somebody important like their boss or their parents, then stand where they can see you, but the others can't, and make a suggestive gesture or pretend to touch yourself intimately – and see if they can keep a straight face, keep up a conversation, or even meet your eye. Teasing is simply great fun if you both get in the swing of it – it is friendly and erotic, suggestive and arousing. The key to good teasing is to pick your moment well – when there's nothing they can do.

• Learn to drive your partner to distraction with subtlety. You can reap your reward later.

Long-distance foreplay

We all go through periods of absence from our lover – and that doesn't mean the foreplay should stop. With modern communications, you should be able to keep the foreplay going all the time.

when they're away

If they're at work, call them up and tell them in explicit and lurid detail exactly what you are going to do to their poor body when they get home. If you've got access to a fax machine, send them a fax of a sexy photograph of yourself with arrows pointing to the bits you want licked/kissed/stroked – but be careful if others in the office can see their faxes; they may not want your intimate details being seen by everyone (on the other hand they may be flattered and pleased). If they have e-mail, send erotic messages. Leave saucy notes for them to find in their briefcase. Put your bedtime CD or tape into their car stereo; if you know they tune in to a certain radio station, send in a message or request using your pet names or a secret code name. Most couples have names for each other's sexual parts: send messages on pagers or mobile phones from these mythical people. Hide a pair of your underpants sprayed with your signature scent in their luggage.

when you're away

If you have to spend a night apart make sure that you leave a sexy note or drawing in their bed so that when they go to sleep they will have a reminder of you. Call them up and tell them how much you are missing them sexually. Send them a bunch of flowers with a note – in code – saying how much you want them to touch you, right *there*.

Write your partner a letter explaining how sexually frustrated you are – and what you've been doing to yourself to relieve that frustration. Send an erotic poem. Go into a photo booth and take a couple of snapshots – see how much you can reveal in the photographs – and then send them to your lover with a note saying that they will be able to see much more when you return.

• Phone sex: talk each other to climax.

Foreplay for fun

Foreplay doesn't have to be serious. You can have foreplay purely for fun.
Fooling around together is very much a part of being in love and being friends.
You can take liberties with each other – and with each other's bodies – that keeps
the passion high and the senses tingling.

sexy shopping

The weekly shopping is boring – we all
know that. So why not spice it up a bit?
Have a competition to see how many
times you can touch each other intimately
in the supermarket – loser buys the coffees
afterward. Or go shopping for clothes
and see if you can both squeeze into the
changing room – and then see what you
can get up to without getting thrown out
of the store.

• A mutual squeeze enlivens the daily round.

sexy games

Remember how to play strip poker? Or strip backgammon? Or backgammon for sexual forfeits? Or chess for sexual dares? If you haven't played a sexy game in ages then do it again soon – they're fun. If you haven't ever, then you have been missing a fun experience. You can play Scrabble™ and use only sexy words. Even Monopoly™ can be spiced up if you use body parts instead of hotels or sexual favors instead of money. If you are fit enough, see how Twister™ compares with the Kama Sutra. There's no limit to the sexy games you can play, and they certainly add a little zing to foreplay.

• Transform the supermarket run with secret fondles.

Ecstatic foreplay

In the previous sections we have looked at foreplay as arousing and teasing. In the next sections we will look at foreplay as it is actually done. How far you go with foreplay – before it becomes lovemaking – is entirely up to you.

how far to go?

Does foreplay always end before orgasm? Is an orgasm a part of sex or foreplay? This is up to you and your lover. Foreplay is preparation for sex, but it is also an art form in its own right. You might like to have the foreplay and let it lead into sex without any break or interruption. You may like to have just the foreplay – for instance, a very pregnant woman may like to stop at just foreplay. And there may be times when you go straight for sex.

there are no rules

How you orgasm, what you need to get there, how often you come, which techniques you use, and what you do during your orgasm are up to you. You don't have to have an orgasm during sex. You don't have to orgasm at the same time. You don't have to orgasm through having sex. You can masturbate, have oral sex, dress up, try different positions, laugh, eat – anything you both want to do is "normal." There are no rules, except ones you both want.

Orgasms

Whether you have an orgasm during your foreplay or not is entirely up to you. You can have as many or as few as you want, when you want, and how you want. Your orgasm is entirely your own business and has nothing to do with anyone else – except, of course, your lover.

a unique opportunity

Bringing your partner to orgasm through foreplay is a unique and valuable experience. You can use it to direct and choreograph the foreplay. You can delay it and then bring them to even greater heights of passion. You can help them to overcome any inhibitions about orgasm by encouraging them to make a noise, thrash around, bite and scratch you as they come, have lots of orgasms, and have

• Orgasm can be the climax of foreplay or lovemaking...

orgasms in all sorts of different ways. Once the trust is there, your lover can relax and begin to experiment. Once they feel free to change what they do to reach orgasm, they can begin to discover all sorts of interesting ways to come – and that means more fun for you as well.

why have one?

Having an orgasm is a completely natural and essential part of any human being's life. We find a release and relaxation in orgasm that isn't available in anything else. Orgasms are beneficial, exciting, recharging, vitalizing, and loving. When we reach orgasm with our lover, we are bonding and cementing our relationship. Our orgasms are a sign of safety and of trust in each other. We might be able to

reach orgasm with a stranger in a one-night stand – but it simply isn't the same as with someone we love.

• ...but coming together is not essential.

Male masturbation

Most men, even in a serious, committed relationship, admit to masturbating themselves. Their partner shouldn't be offended or feel it is a betrayal of their relationship or sexuality. Sometimes the man may masturbate with, or next to, his partner, and other times they may masturbate alone.

quite normal

Men don't go mad, go blind, or get hairy palms from masturbating. They won't lose their "vital energy," their sleep, or their souls through masturbation. It is a normal, natural, and essential part of adult sexuality. And male masturbation with a partner is normal and healthy. There is nothing wrong about masturbating in front of your lover – or being masturbated by your lover.

how to do it

Most men find masturbating quite easy. It's something they've done regularly since their early teens. Some women, however, find it a little difficult initially to masturbate their male lover. This is because the technique isn't as easy as it looks. The best way for a woman to learn is for her partner to do it and for her to watch. Once you have learned the basic technique – how much pressure to use, the rhythm he likes, the speed he needs – you can then begin to vary it. You might like to try using two hands, or using a twisting motion, or slowing the tempo just as he comes to see what effect it has, or pulling the foreskin back (assuming he has one) just as he comes. Experiment, have fun. You may excite yourself to orgasm as well.

• A delicate touch is a tantalizing asset when bringing your lover to climax.

Female masturbation

There is still a myth that women don't masturbate as much as men. The evidence, though, seems to be that women masturbate just as frequently. They may be a little more discreet and not talk about it quite as freely.

what a woman needs

Most men may be pleasantly surprised to find that women enjoy pleasuring themselves as much as men do. But a woman masturbating in front of her male lover needs to feel safe and relaxed. She needs to feel that she is loved and wanted. She needs to feel sexy and desirable. And most of all, she needs to feel that what she is doing is not wrong, dirty, abnormal, or disgusting. If she has been brought up to believe that any of these things is true,

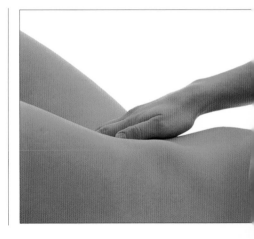

then she may not be as relaxed and open as she might like to be. And it is important for her lover not to betray her trust. He must be careful to encourage and support her openness.

• Most women appreciate a slow hand.

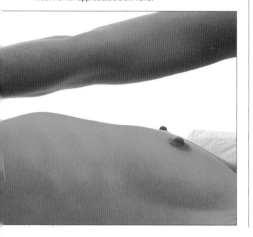

what a man needs to do

You can't masturbate your female partner successfully and considerately if you don't know what she wants, needs, and likes. Get her to do it and learn from what she does. Some women need their clitoris stimulated hard and fast; for others this is completely wrong and they need it slow and gentle. All women are different in the way they masturbate, whereas men are fairly similar in that they need pressure, friction, and climactic speed. You will learn from your lover only if you don't assume you know what they need. Women tend to take longer to orgasm than men, so be patient and don't rush anything – it's all pleasurable and enjoyable. If you take your time, you may be able to share her multiple orgasms rippling under your fingers.

Mutual masturbation

Mutual masturbation isn't an alternative to sex – it is sex. It is ideal when a couple are tired and haven't the stamina for sex, or when the woman is very pregnant. Or you can do it just for fun.

setting goals

Some people find mutual masturbation difficult to do. They think it is perhaps a little insulting to prefer it to "real sex." It's not. If you and your partner are truly in touch – emotionally and sexually – you will know when pleasing each other this way will work. It makes a great overture to full sex. The myths about mutual masturbation are many – you both have to come, you have to do it simultaneously – and they are all myths. How a couple choose to masturbate each other is entirely up to them. It is probably better if they take turns – this allows them to be free to enjoy their own orgasm without having to concentrate on giving the other pleasure. There's nothing quite so disconcerting as being ready to reach orgasm yourself and having your partner break off masturbating you to reach their own orgasm. On the other hand, it can be fun sometimes. Don't set goals – allow what happens to happen.

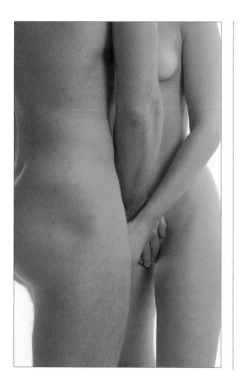

getting in a rut

The only rule about mutual masturbation – or any other form of foreplay – is to vary what you do in order to avoid getting into a rut. If one partner always comes first, the other has the joy of not having to do anything afterward. This simply isn't fair. Vary who comes first. Sometimes, as a special treat, masturbate your partner and then masturbate yourself while they watch and relax, knowing they're "off duty" and can rest. Give your partner lots of time to recover from their own orgasm before giving you yours – allow them time to enjoy their afterglow without any pressure; be patient. Your time (and your turn) will come.

• Pleasing each other by touch alone is a loving way to explore each other's bodies.

Oral sex for her

Some men don't like performing oral sex on their female partner – and they are missing out on a lot. A woman can help by reassuring him that she is showered, clean, and fresh, so he won't find anything inhibiting on that score. And she can encourage him a lot.

what a man should do

Most women enjoy oral sex and like the sensation of having their clitoris and labia licked and sucked. You should begin slowly and gently, teasing the area around her clitoris with your tongue. You can put your tongue inside her vagina, but do it gently at first. You can also use your fingers. If you pull back on her pubic bone, you will increase the area available to be licked and heighten the sensations. Take your time. You might like to put a pillow under her hips to raise her vulva and make it more accessible. Oral sex can be tiring, so vary what you are doing and don't be afraid to take a break to rest your tongue. Use your lips as well, to suck on her clitoris, and keep asking to see if what you are doing is right for her. She may tell you, or you may be able to read the signals. Don't ever be tempted to blow air into a woman's vagina.

what a woman shouldn't do

Don't suffocate your partner. Open your thighs wide enough for him to get air. Give him room to breathe. Let him rest occasionally. Give him lots of information, either by telling him or moving appropriately, so that he can please you better. Don't expect him to get it right the first time, or every time. Don't insist if he seems disinclined at first. Give it time.

• Oral sex is more satisfying if the woman is relaxed after foreplay.

Oral sex for him

For a man, having his lover perform oral sex on him is erotic, flattering, and sensuous, as well as being completely normal and clean. It is something that most men enjoy and most women like to do for their lover. It shouldn't take the place of sex, though, but be a normal, sexy part of foreplay.

what a woman should do

Contrary to popular terminology, there is nothing about blowing in oral sex. There's lots of sucking and rubbing, but no blowing – since that could be dangerous. For most men, the pressure of lips and sucking alone aren't sufficient to bring them to orgasm, so you may have to masturbate him with your hand as well. Whether you let him come in your mouth is entirely up to you, as is whether you swallow his semen. If you choose not to do either, then don't, but don't act as if the idea is revolting or abnormal – just don't do it. If you keep your hand around his penis as you suck, you can also control the amount of thrusting he can do, and this can save you from gagging if he thrusts deep. You might try letting his semen spray over your breasts and then let him slowly rub it in. Or stroke some over his stomach and massage him with it.

what a man shouldn't do

Don't demand oral sex – it's a privilege and a mark of intimacy, not a right. Don't thrust too much or your partner may gag. Establish etiquette beforehand. Make it clear whether you enjoy the occasional nibble, prefer teeth just to graze your penis, or want no biting at all. You should also know what your partner wants to do when you come. Don't ejaculate in her mouth if she doesn't want you to. Don't expect her to swallow your semen; if she does it's because she chooses to, not because you pressure her to. If she gets tired or runs out of stamina, let her take a break or switch what you are doing. Don't hold her head tightly against your groin.

• Oral sex with a lover is highly erotic for a man, and most women enjoy giving pleasure too.

Tantric foreplay

Tantras are texts written about the spiritual aspects of sex: sex used as a means of communicating with God, sex used to achieve some sort of spiritual enlightenment. This is great if you have the time and inclination. But what is really useful is that many tantric writings contain lots of lovely things you can do to spice up your foreplay – without having to go to India, where most tantric texts are found.

the kama sutra

The most famous Indian sex manual, which everyone has heard about, is the *Kama Sutra*. It lists over a hundred different positions for sex. Some of them are quite bizarre and you would need to be a contortionist (or do advanced yoga) to do them – and some are quite interesting. They have fascinating names, such as the congress of the bull, the congress of the elephant, and the congress of the monkey (congress simply means intercourse). Get a copy and try a different position every night.

the perfumed garden and the ananga ranga

Or get a copy of the *Perfumed Garden*. This is an Arabian book that contains eleven positions, some of which are similar to ones in the *Kama Sutra*. Or there's the *Ananga Ranga*, which is another Indian book that goes into considerable detail about how to improve orgasm through yoga exercises. These books, suitably translated, are widely available and should provide you with considerable entertainment, fun, and new ideas. Tantric foreplay should be done with an open mind – follow the instructions and see what happens. Their main aim is a spiritual orgasm, which we will look at next.

• Tantric positions can help you prolong foreplay and delay orgasm.

Spiritual orgasms

Most tantric texts claim that a man's orgasm has two parts – the physical ejaculation and the spiritual orgasm. They claim it isn't necessary for him to ejaculate to have an orgasm – he can stop at what they call the plateau of delight. He may even be able to go higher and higher, and have multiple "spiritual" orgasms.

what to do

Whether any of this is true doesn't matter – it's a lot of fun trying it out just to see if there's anything to it. We look at ways of delaying orgasm in the next section; what we will look at here are ways of enhancing the orgasm to make it more spiritual. One of the most interesting is called, in the tantric texts, soul gathering. Here you look deeply into your lover's eyes as they orgasm – you gather their soul as it unites with their body in climax. Another way is to attempt to orgasm together, deliberately, just to see what happens to your energy if you hold each other tightly as you both come – or look into each other's eyes, or suck on each other's tongues. The idea is to prevent sexual energy from escaping through the top of your head. You will need to use whatever method suits you to achieve this, and it's good fun even if you don't take it seriously.

cold sex

One aspect of tantric sex is the recommendation to avoid passion and try cold sex. You make an appointment, get together, and have sex. It's quite remote and without emotion but very exciting to try. Practicing tantric sex definitely has something to recommend it as long as it is done in a spirit of fun and exploration.

Read books about it together; the techniques will give you new ideas of how to please each other.

• Simply looking deep into your partner's eyes, plunging into their soul, can trigger orgasm.

Delaying orgasm

You might think an orgasm is something not to be delayed – something to be enjoyed at once. However, if we want our foreplay to continue – and the passion and excitement to keep building – it might be desirable to learn how to delay orgasm. Deferred gratification can be fun.

why delay?

For women, delaying orgasm isn't so necessary. They can have several or multiple orgasms without losing their enthusiasm or desire. For men it is different. The orgasm, enjoyable as it might be, often signals the end of lovemaking for them – at least for a while. If the man learns how to delay his orgasm he can keep his partner happier for longer – and that will be good for him as well.

techniques

The easiest for the man to learn is the squeeze technique. When he can feel himself coming he, or his partner, squeezes the penis quite hard just below its head. Different men need different pressure for this technique to work successfully. Alternatively, he might like to try pressing hard with his index finger on his perineum – the area of skin between the anus and the scrotum. Both of these techniques require experimentation to find the right pressure and place. The man might also like to try the "locking" method. When he is close to orgasm he can almost withdraw, suck in his lower abdomen, and arch his back – thus locking himself up. This works well with a little practice but it does require him to stop thrusting for a while as he does it. Some tantric sex books teach effective techniques for delaying orgasms.

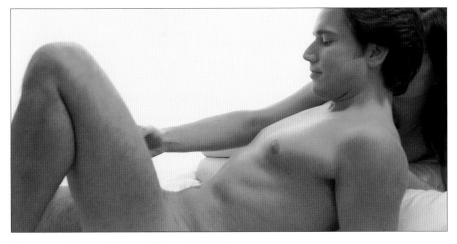

• The squeeze technique can delay orgasm. Get your partner to help!

Afterplay/ready to begin again

If, after sex or foreplay, we curl up and go to sleep, then that is the end of sex for that session. If, however, we stay awake, keep talking, keep stroking, touching and kissing, our arousal gradually builds up again and we can keep going.

why keep going?

Everybody has different sexual needs – and we have to be considerate and aware of our lover's needs. We may like to have a quick orgasm and go to sleep, but our partner may want more holding, or take longer to get aroused, or need more orgasms than us. They may want to stay intimate and close for longer, have better stamina and staying power, recover more quickly, and be ready for more, more frequently. Or our lover might be the one who wants to go to sleep right away. So how do we keep them awake long enough to satisfy us? What is the secret?

• Restore your energies with luxurious tastes before you begin again

keep touching

You have already read the techniques for delaying orgasm for men, so you might be experimenting with that. You can also practice staying in touch – literally, physically. Snuggle up. If you allow too much space, it will be filled with sleep; keep holding each other; keep kiss-ing; keep fondling each other. If you let go, the feeling will go. If you keep fondling, the desire will return much more quickly. It's also nice to keep touching our lover after sex or foreplay – it's a reminder that we are together.